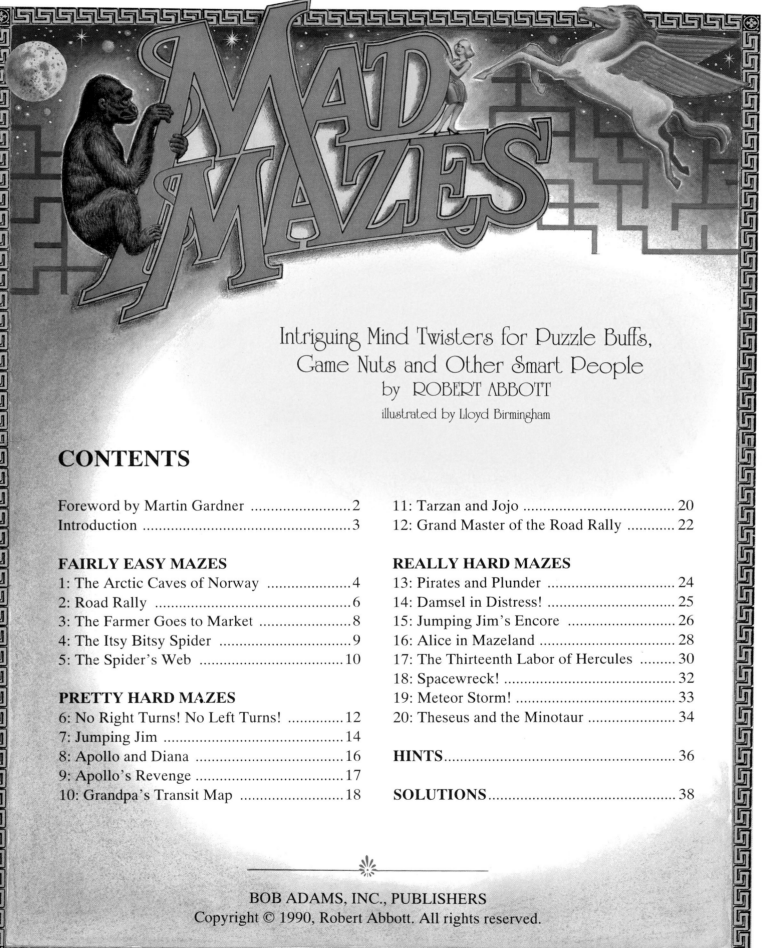

MAD MAZES

Intriguing Mind Twisters for Puzzle Buffs,
Game Nuts and Other Smart People
by ROBERT ABBOTT

illustrated by Lloyd Birmingham

CONTENTS

BOB ADAMS, INC., PUBLISHERS

Foreword

Inventing a new kind of puzzle, not too hard, not too easy, and fun to crack, is a much harder task than solving such puzzles. Robert Abbott is one of those rare individuals who has the knack of creating such puzzles. How he does it is a mystery.

I first met Bob when I was writing the Mathematical Games column in *Scientific American.* He had invented a card game called Eleusis that had the remarkable property of simulating induction, the process by which scientific laws are discovered and theories formulated. My two columns on Eleusis were among the most popular. They led to other induction games, and even to some interesting research on induction. In 1963 Bob wrote *Abbott's New Card Games* (alas, now out of print) that included Eleusis among other unusual games.

No one has been as creative as Bob in devising bizarre mazes that are unlike any you have seen before. These mazes, let me add, also have an affinity with scientific method. What is science if not the trying of every possible path that can lead to the solution of a puzzle posed by Nature? When researchers reach a blind alley, they sigh and turn back to try other paths.

Bob's mazes will not advance science or mathematics, but in working on them you will experience a pleasure that in its small way is similar to the pleasure experienced by scientists when they solve a problem. Think of the maze as a model of a tiny portion of a perhaps infinite universe — out there, independent of you and me — with uncountable labyrinths waiting to be explored.

Martin Gardner

INTRODUCTION

This book is a collection of mazes that are not at all like conventional mazes. A conventional paper-and-pencil maze looks something like this:

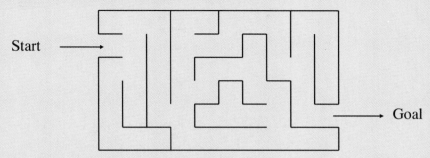

It is essentially a map of what could have been an outdoor, walk- through maze.

The mazes in this book are very different. Each has a set of weird rules—and the weirder the better—that determine how you can move through the maze. I'm not sure whether these should be called puzzles or mazes, but they have the look and feel of mazes, and they create the same delightful feelings of confusion and disorientation that you experience in a maze.

You might think of these mazes as interesting places to get lost in. I hope you will find it amusing just to wander through a maze for a while before you concentrate too hard on finding the solution. There are, actually, a lot of different ways to approach these mazes. For example, a friend of mine, Bob Wittrock, who is an operations researcher at IBM, is only interested in creating systems that guarantee a mechanical solution to a maze. Of course, once he has such a system, there's not really any point in solving the maze. But he's not interested in the solution; he's interested in creating a system to find the solution. Wittrock, incidentally, helped me in thinking up a lot of the rules for these mazes. And, while I'm making acknowledgments, I'd like to thank Jim Adams, who worked out several of the stories for the mazes.

Whatever way you approach these mazes, at some point you'll no doubt want to find the solution. You'll then discover that the mazes can be pretty hard—well, some of them are almost impossible. You should allow at least a day or two to find any solution.

I've provided a section of hints; so if you're about to give up on a maze, try the hint for the maze before you read the solution. Some of the hints have interesting information about the maze; so you might look at a hint even after you've solved a maze. For instance, in the hint for Maze 7, I present one of Wittrock's mechanical methods for finding a solution.

The mazes are presented in their approximate order of difficulty. (The order is approximate because I can't make an exact estimate of the difficulty of any maze.) You don't have to go through the book in numeric order, but you'll have a better chance of solving the harder mazes near the end if you start with some of the easier mazes near the beginning.

Some of these mazes first appeared quite a while ago. Mazes 3 and 4 were in Martin Gardner's "Mathematical Games" columns in the October 1962 and November 1963 issues of *Scientific American*. (The versions of the mazes in *Scientific American* had the same rules but different layouts. After all these years I found I could improve on the layouts.) A variation of Maze 18 first appeared in the November 1982 issue of *Games*. Recently, Mazes 6, 12, 13, and 15 appeared in *Discover* magazine.

—Robert Abbott
New York, New York

THE ARCTIC CAVES OF NORWAY

Caught in a winter blizzard while on a ski trip across northern Norway, Lars Skaldheim sought shelter in a nearby cave. However, a sudden avalanche blocked the entrance, trapping Lars in the cave. Lars can escape if he can get to an exit that's on the other side of the mountain.

Unfortunately, some parts of the cave (the areas shown in blue on the map) have showers of icy waters from glacial streams. Other parts (the areas shown in red on the map) are filled with steam from underground hot springs. Lars can run through either area, but if he ran through two icy areas in succession he would freeze solid, and if he ran through two of the steamy areas in succession, he would be cooked alive. He can, however, pass through as many of these areas as he wishes as long as he alternates between cold and hot areas. (Incidentally—just in case you thought of trying this—Lars may not make a U-turn when he is running through one of the cold or hot areas.)

Can you find a way that Lars can escape from the cave?

MAD MAZE 2

Road Rally

The small town of Oxbridge, Ohio was host to the spring rally of the Southern Ohio Auto Club. The Grand Marshal for the event, Russell Whitehead, decided that the rally would be a test of logical ability as well as driving skill. On the night before the rally he painted a large red or green arrow on every block of Oxbridge.

The drivers entered town at the point marked START on the map shown here. Each driver was given a sheet of paper with these instructions: "You have to travel from this point to the Skyline Cafe, where we'll all meet and have some Cincinnati style 5-way chili. U-turns or backing up is not allowed, and you must stay on the blocks with arrows—you can't go off onto any of the driveways. If a block has a double-headed arrow, you can travel on that block in either direction. If a block has a single-headed arrow, you can only travel in the direction of the arrow. And there's one final restriction: after you travel down a block with a red arrow, you can then only go down a block with a green arrow; and after a green arrow, you can only go down a block with a red arrow."

The rally was won by Linda Weisenheimer, who was already on her second bowl of chili before any other drivers reached the cafe. Can you discover a route that Linda could have taken to reach the goal?

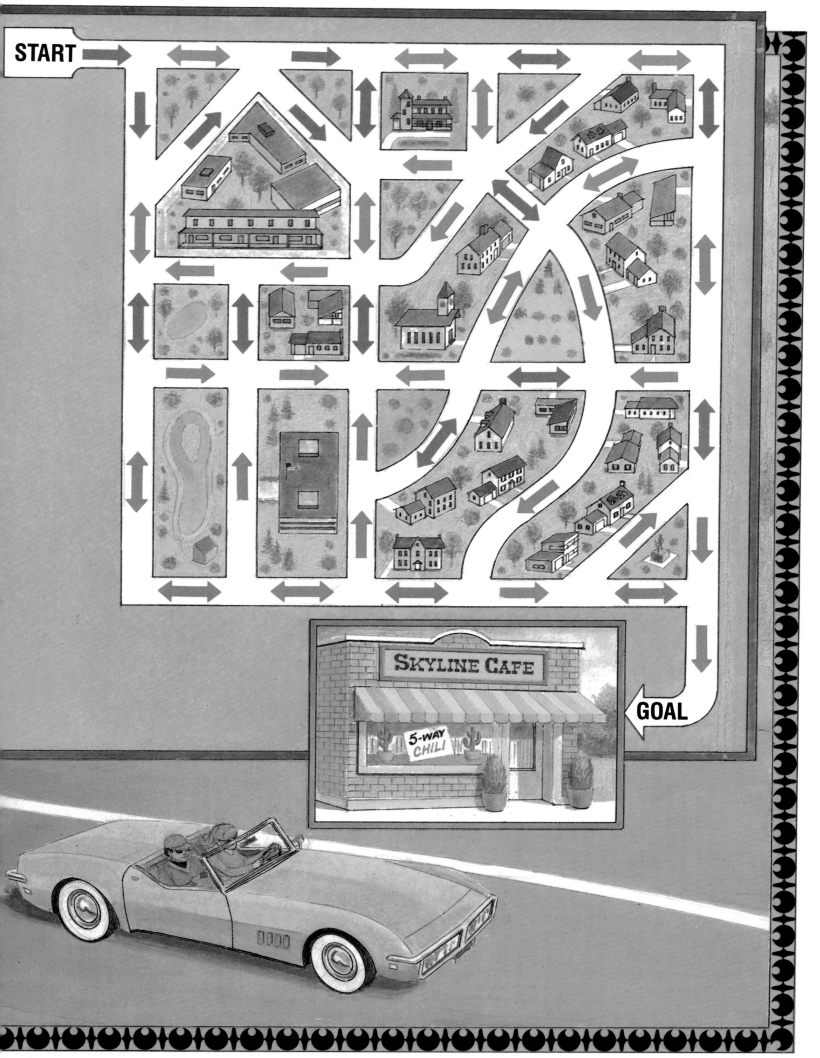

START

SKYLINE CAFE

5-WAY CHILI

GOAL

MAD MAZE 3

THE FARMER GOES TO MARKET

Because the town of Floyd's Knob, Indiana, had only 37 registered automobiles, the mayor thought it would be safe to appoint his cousin, Henry Stables, who was the town cutup, as its traffic commissioner. But he soon regretted his decision. When the town awoke one morning, it found that a profusion of signs had been erected establishing confusing restrictions on turns at every intersection in town.

The citizens were all for tearing down these signs until the police chief, another cousin of the mayor, made a surprising discovery. Motorists passing through town became so exasperated that sooner or later they made a prohibited turn. The police chief found that the town was making even more money from these violations than from its speed trap on an outlying country road.

Of course everyone was overjoyed, particularly because the next day was Saturday and Moses MacAdam, the county's richest farmer, was due to pass through town on his way to the county seat. They expected to extract a large fine from Moses, believing it to be impossible to drive through town without at least one traffic violation. But Moses had been secretly studying the signs. When Saturday morning came, he astonished the entire town by driving from his farm through town to the county seat without a single violation!

Can you discover a route that Moses could have taken? Enter town on the road at the left and exit on the road at the right. At each intersection you must follow one of the arrows. That is, you may turn in a given direction only when there is a curved line in that direction, and you may go straight only when there is a straight line to follow. You may leave an intersection only at the head of an arrow. U-turns or backing up is not allowed.

As you can see, at the first intersection you can only go straight. At the second intersection you encounter you can again only go straight. At the third intersection you can go straight or turn north. Suppose you turn north. At the next intersection you can only turn east. True, there is a line that curves to the west, but there's no arrowhead pointing west, so you can't leave that intersection in a westerly direction.

In this map, and in the other city maps in the book, there are driveways drawn inside the blocks. The driveways are only decorative; you can't use them as part of your route through a maze.

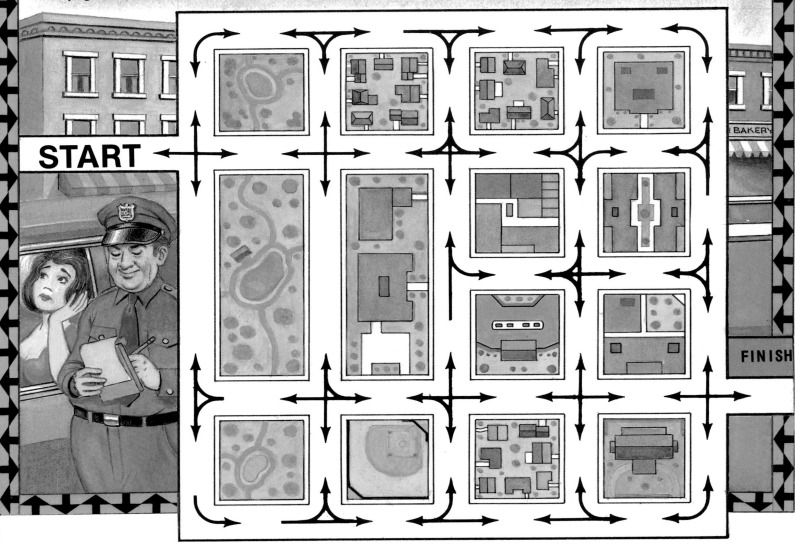

START

FINISH

The Itsy Bitsy Spider

Fred was discussing a problem with his architect:

"I have a terrible itsy bitsy spider infestation. Actually, it's only one itsy bitsy spider, but he's very persistent. He spins a web on the roof that clogs up the gutter. When it rains, he is washed down the water spout. But then along comes the sun and dries up all the rain and the itsy bitsy spider climbs up the spout again. And there's not a damn thing I can do about it."

"Don't worry," said the architect. "He may be persistent but spiders aren't that bright. I suggest we put a maze at the bottom of the water spout; then the spider won't be able to find his way back up."

The architect came back the next day with the diagram shown at the right. "What I propose is this: we run the water spout into a large metal box. The box will contain many small chambers on five levels. The water will come in at the top, on Level A, will travel from chamber to chamber, and will drain out at this opening on Level E. There has to be a path through the box, otherwise the water won't be able to drain through. But I've made the path very complicated. Once the spider gets washed out of the opening on Level E, he won't be able to

figure out how to get back through the box and back into the water spout.

"The solid black lines represent walls, which the spider cannot get through. I've used yellow to indicate floors. If the spider's on a yellow square, he cannot travel from that point down to the next level. If a square is not colored yellow, then he can travel down to the corresponding square in the level below. To figure out whether the spider can travel *up*, you have to check out the corresponding square in the level above. If that square has no floor, then the spider can travel up. If the square does have a floor (that is, it's colored yellow), then the spider cannot travel up."

"This sounds like a perfectly reasonable plan to me," said Fred. "In fact, I can't figure out how to get through the box myself." So, they built the box and added it to the water spout. The first rainstorm did wash the spider through the box, but, unfortunately, after the sun dried up the rain the spider went back into the box, traveled through it and back up the water spout. Can you discover a path the spider could take to get through the box? You have to go in the entrance on Level E and then work your way up to the water spout on Level A.

MAD MAZE 5

THE SPIDER'S WEB

I.B. Spider (better known to us as the itsy bitsy spider) has spun this web and caught a whole lot of disgusting but quite yummy bugs. One day he sees that a lady spider has entered his web. I.B. decides to go over to the lady spider and ask her out for dinner.

I.B. Spider has a problem, though. He can only travel around his web by making a series of moves. Each move must be in a straight line, and each move must travel over two bugs and end at the third bug. (Despite the best efforts of many scientists, exactly why this breed of spiders moves in this way is still unknown.)

I.B. begins at the upper left. From there his first move will take him to the bug marked Bug A. He is now at an intersection and his next move could take him forward to Bug B, or he could go south to Bug C, or he could move southwest to Bug D.

The lady spider is at the bottom of the web. I.B. must reach her at the end of a move; therefore, he must somehow find his way to Bug E, which is the third bug away from the lady spider.

So: how can I.B. Spider use his maze-threading abilities to reach the lady spider? And will she really have dinner with him?

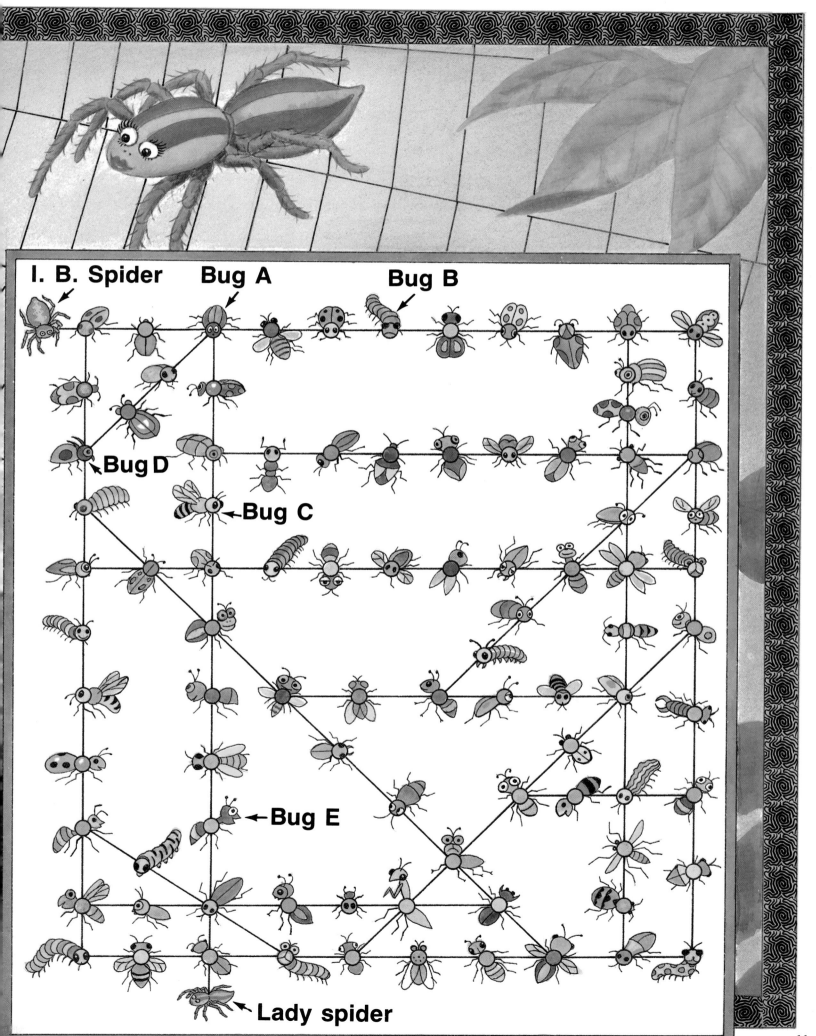

I. B. Spider Bug A Bug B

Bug D

Bug C

Bug E

Lady spider

11

No Left Turns!/No Right Turns!

6

Phil bought a new car equipped with Super Dynacomp, a state-of- the-art, computer-controlled steering system. He only had the car a week when it developed a strange bug: he could drive straight or turn right, but the steering system wouldn't let him make a left turn.

Phil was able to drive back to his house and he called Carl's Auto Repair. Carl said he knew what the problem was, and he explained it as follows:

"Every car in town that has Super Dynacomp has the same problem. It starts when you drive along the block past the power station. [That block is shown with a jagged red line on the map.] The power station is experiencing a serious leakage of current now. The current jolts the Super Dynacomp computer and it loses the ability to turn left.

What's really weird is that if you go down that block another time—in either direction—then the computer gets a second jolt that restores the ability to turn left, but it now loses the ability to turn right. Go down the block again, and you're back to only driving straight or turning right. Each time you go down the block, you switch between these two states. If you bring the car in, we can fix it."

Phil said he would drive there right away, but as soon as he hung up, he realized he had a problem. With his steering behaving in such a strange fashion, he wasn't sure he could make it to Carl's Auto Repair. He got out his town map, spent at least an hour puzzling over it, and the he finally figured out how he could get to Carl's.

Can you find a route Phil could take? You leave Phil's house on a road shown with an arrow, and you enter Carl's Auto Repair by another road with an arrow. Initially you can only go straight or turn right. U-turns or backing up is not allowed, and you can't go off the main roads onto any of the driveways or paths shown inside the blocks. As you can probably guess, you're going to have to drive down the block with the jagged red line. The first time you do that, be sure to start only turning left or going straight. That may be a little hard to visualize after you've gotten used to only going straight or right. If you go down that block again, be sure to switch back to only going straight or right, and subsequently you should switch each time you go down the block.

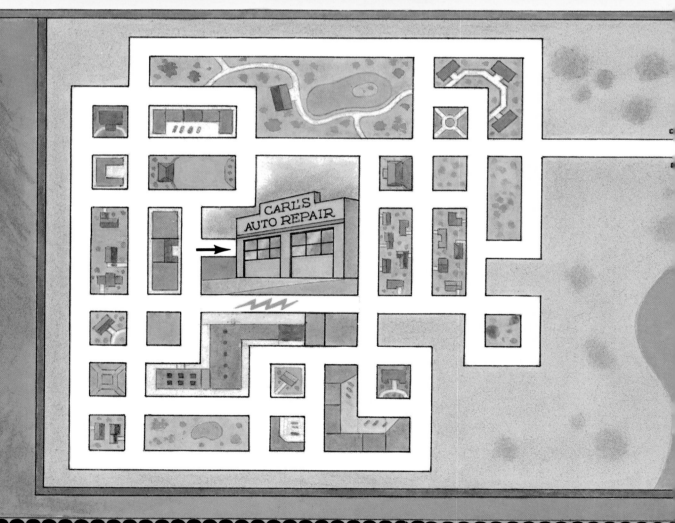

Jumping Jim is about to begin his grand performance at the circus, but his jealous enemy, Dastardly Dan, has restrung all the trampolines. The number on each trampoline indicates how tightly strung each one is; in other words, the number indicates how far Jim will move (horizontally or vertically, but *not* diagonally) when he bounces off the trampoline. Jim begins his routine by leaping onto the trampoline at the upper left. He must get to the Goal at the lower right, where he will take his bow. How can he get there?

The diagram at the right shows all the trampolines with each represented as a square. Begin on the square at the upper left. That square is marked *3*. From there you could, for example, move three squares down to a square marked *2*. From there, you might move two squares right to a square marked *4*, and from there you could move four squares right to another square marked *2*. That path, incidentaliy, won't get you to the goal.

START

Apollo, god of the sun, stole a set of arrows from his sister Diana, goddess of the moon. When Diana caught him shooting moonbeams instead of sunbeams, she was furious! She cast a mighty curse, and all his arrows fell around him in a terrible maze. That maze is shown here. Apollo's sunbeams are the red arrows; Diana's moonbeams are the blue arrows.

Diana spoke to Apollo: "You will remain here in this field of arrows until you solve this puzzle. You must find a route from the red arrow at the upper left to the bull's-eye at the lower right. The first red arrow points to two blue arrows. Choose either of those blue arrows and move to it. You are now on a blue arrow that points to one or more red arrows. Choose one of those red arrows and move to it. Continue in this fashion, alternating between red and blue arrows. If you are truly wise you will arrive at an arrow that points to the bull's-eye. You

may then proceed to the bull's-eye and escape from the maze. It's far more likely, though, that you will wander into a loop and find yourself going around endlessly. If that happens, you can admit that you are lost, go back to the red arrow at the upper left, and start the puzzle over again."

So, how can Apollo find his way to the bull's-eye (without getting stuck in too many loops)?

Apollo's Revenge

START

After several days, Apollo escaped from the arrow maze that his sister had placed him in, and after his long entrapment he was determined to have his revenge. He created his own maze out of the arrows, and then hid nearby. When his sister came to check on her captive, he leapt out of hiding, overpowered her, and threw her into the maze of arrows.

He cried out to her: "You will remain here until you solve this puzzle as I had to. As before, you must start on the red arrow at the upper left, travel from red arrow, to

blue arrow, to red arrow, and so forth, until you come to an arrow that lets you move towards the bull's eye."

"But that's not all," gloated Apollo. "Because I am so very clever, I added a new rule that will utterly confuse you. When you begin the maze, you move in the directions that the arrows point; that is, you move where the *head* of an arrow points. When you land on an arrow inside of a circle, you start moving in the *opposite* direction. Beginning at the arrow in the circle, move

in the direction pointed to by the *tail* of the arrow. On subsequent arrows, continue moving where the tails point until you again stop on an arrow in a circle. At that point, switch back to moving where the *heads* point. Thus, each time you stop on an arrow in a circle, you change whether you follow heads or tails. Just passing *over* a circle has no effect on your movement."

Is Apollo's new rule really that confusing? If not, can you find your way through this maze?

Grandpa's Transit Map

On winter nights years ago when it was too cold and snowy to go outside, Grandpa would tell us stories of his youth:

"I grew up in Lignite County, Pennsylvania, which just happened to have the weirdest transit system in the United States. Here's a map I saved that shows what the system was like in 1910. I was thirteen years old then." Grandpa's map is shown on the next page.

"The circles are the villages of Lignite County, and the colored lines are the transit lines. None of the lines ran through a village. Instead, they only took you to the village center. If you wanted to travel further, you had to change to another line.

"We had four *types* of transit lines. They are shown on the map like this:

Horse car lines: ┼┼┼┼┼┼

Cable car lines: ∿∿∿∿

Trolley lines: ———

Bus lines: – – – –

Three different companies ran these transit lines. We always referred to them as the Red, the Blue, and the Green companies, since those colors were used on the map to show which company ran which line.

"There was a system of free transfers between lines, but it was pretty complicated. Transfers were allowed only at the village centers. Each of the three companies allowed free transfers between its lines. So, if you came into a village on, for example, a Blue line, you could leave the village on another Blue line. Also, the county government had passed a law that the companies had to accept transfers from the same *type* of line. So, if you came into a village on, say, a Red trolley line, then you could make a free transfer to a Blue trolley line or to a Green trolley line (or you could also transfer to a different Red trolley line).

"You were not allowed to ride a line into a village, do some shopping, then use your free transfer to get back on the line you used to enter the village. However, we found that sometimes there were tricky ways to avoid paying an extra fare. Suppose you had just taken the Red cable car line from Crumbsburg, east to Klutztown." Grandpa drew the names of these two villages on the map.

"You cannot now use a free transfer to take the cable car line back west to Crumbsburg. But you can do the following: Use your free transfer to get on the Red

horse car line that goes east to the next village. Then transfer to the Green horse car line that goes south-east. At the next village, transfer to the Blue horse car line that goes west. Then transfer to the Blue bus line going west, and then transfer to the Red bus line going north. You're now back in Klutztown, and since you arrived on the Red bus line you can now transfer to the Red cable car line and take it back west to Crumbsburg.

"One day during the summer of 1910, I visited the county fair at Startsburg. When I was ready to go back to our home in Endenville, I discovered that I had spent all my money except for one nickel. The nickel was just enough to pay my fare on the Red cable car line that left Startsburg, but I would have to use free transfers to get to Endenville. After studying the map a long time, I figured out a way I could get to Endenville using only free transfers. I had to ride so many different lines that by the time I got home it was almost midnight. But I was pretty proud of myself for figuring this out."

How could Grandpa have gotten from Startsburg to Endenville on only one fare?

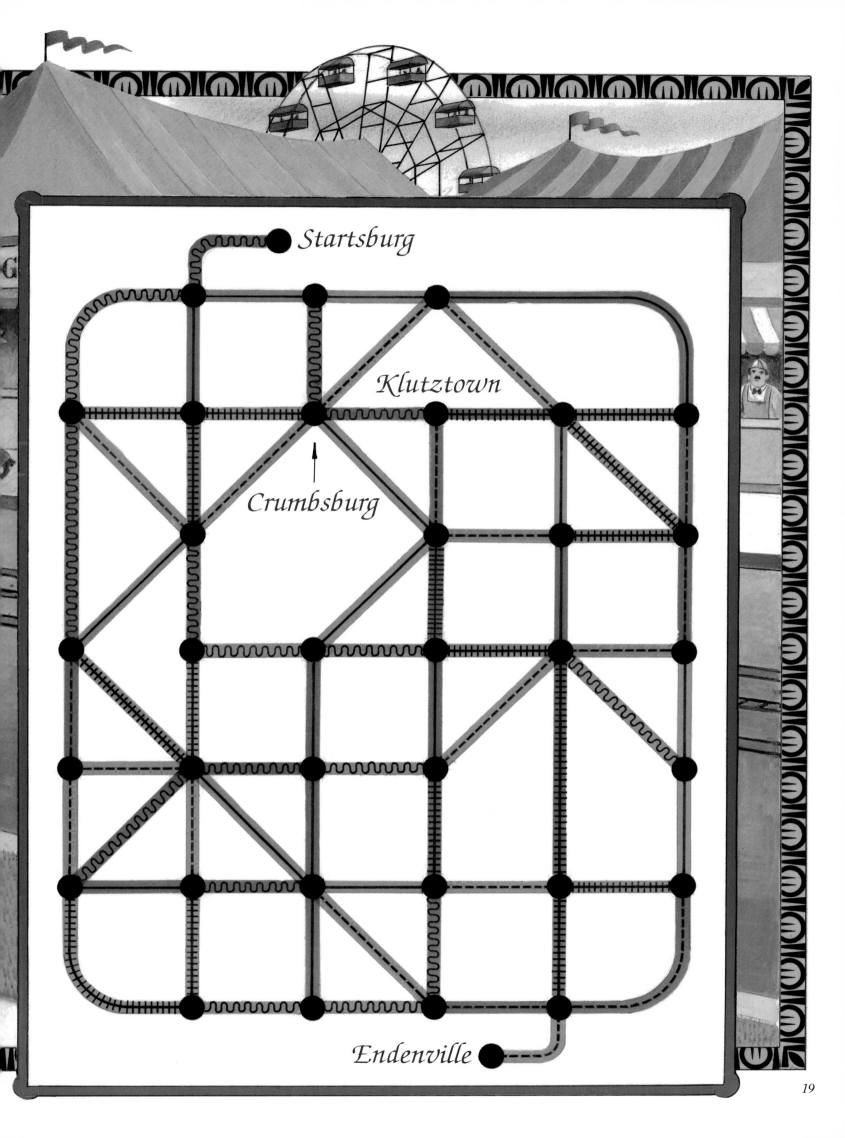

Startsburg

Klutztown

Crumbsburg

Endenville

MAD MAZE

11

Tarzan and Jojo

Tarzan was spending a peaceful day in the jungle when his friend Jojo the chimpanzee began taunting him. "You can't catch me, ape-man," shouted Jojo. Tarzan, always one to enjoy a good chase, began swinging after him, only to find that Jojo had tangled up all of the hanging tree vines. Therefore, as Tarzan swings through the jungle, he can only move in the direction of the arrow in the square at the beginning of each swing. And because of the length of the vines, each swing must carry him exactly three or four squares.

Tarzan begins on the square at the top. From there he can travel three squares to A or go four squares to B. Suppose he goes to square B. On the next turn he can only go three squares to C (from B it is impossible to travel four squares). From square C he can go three squares to D or four squares to E.

Jojo has hidden in the square at the bottom of his maze of vines. How can Tarzan get to that square? (Note that only one square, the one marked F, will enable Tarzan to swing onto Jojo's square.)

Grand Master of the Road Rally

Linda Weisenheimer was appointed Grand Master of the fall rally of the Southern Ohio Auto Club. You will recall that she had been the winner of the spring rally that was immortalized in Maze 2.

Linda decided that the fall rally would be another test of logical ability, except that this rally would be about ten times as complex as the spring rally. She arranged for the rally to be held in the city of Loydsville. On the night before the rally, she painted large red letters on many blocks of the city. A map of Loydsville with Linda's letters is shown here.

The drivers entered Loydsville at the point marked START, and each was given a sheet of paper with these instructions: "You must travel from this point to the goal, which is the Loydsville branch of the University of Ohio. The first driver there will receive an honorary degree in logic. As you travel down certain blocks you will pass various red letters. After you've traveled past an A, you're not allowed to travel past any letter except a B. After you've traveled past a B, you then can only travel past a C. After a C, you can only travel past a D. And after you've traveled

past a D, you can then only travel past an A. You must keep on the streets—you can't use any of the driveways."

Everyone complimented Linda on the creation of a brilliant puzzle. But then they all spent the rest of the day circling around Loydsville and by sundown no one had figured out how to get to the goal. Everyone decided to go home, and at the next meeting a motion to expel Linda from the club was only narrowly defeated.

If you had been at this rally, could you have found the route to the goal? There really is a way to get there.

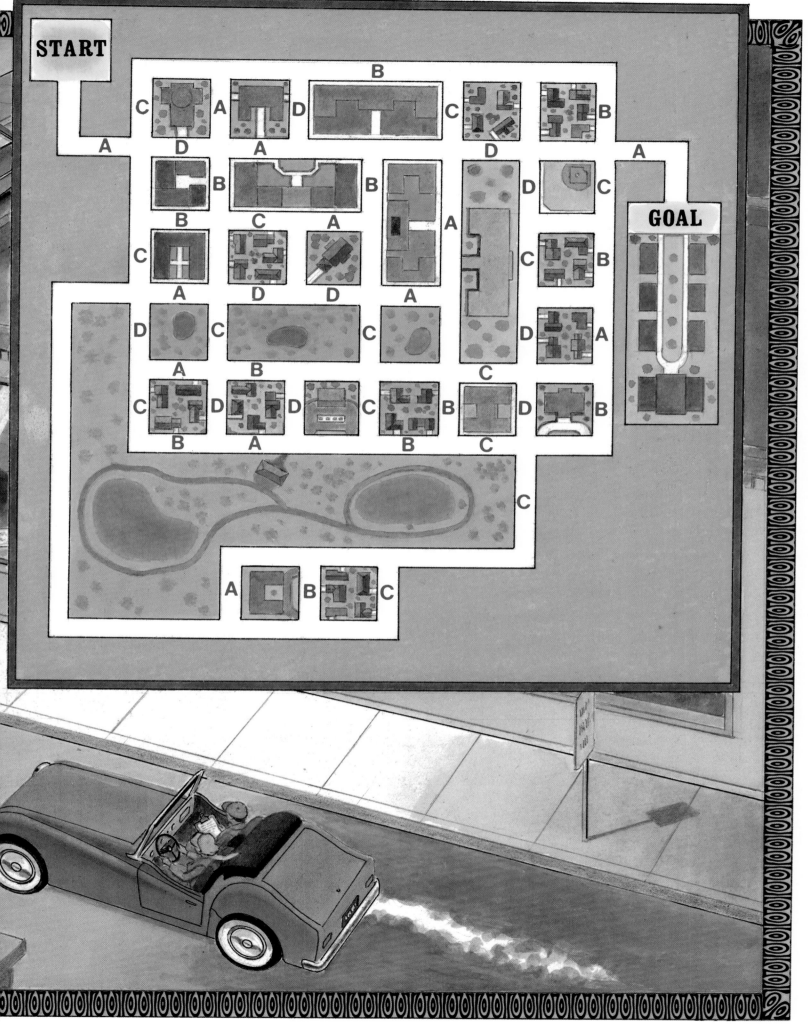

23

PIRATES and PLUNDER

Captain Long John Silver was gambling with his first mate, Jack the Hook, and losing heavily. The captain had wagered everything he had (and a lot he didn't have), and now Jack wanted him to pay up. In desperation, Captain Silver made a bargain with his mate: Silver would draw a map made entirely of dice. If Jack could find the correct route through this map, the captain would pay him everything he owed and also tell him the location of his buried treasure. But if Jack could not find the route, then Silver owed him nothing. Jack the Hook, being as greedy as the next pirate, agreed to the deal.

So, on the back of his treasure map, Captain Silver drew the diagram of dice that is shown here. On the red five in the center he placed his lucky die, with the six on top and the four facing the bottom of the

map. The object, said the captain, is simply to move the die off the center square, then find a way to move it back onto the center square.

Jack thought that sounded pretty easy, but then the captain added more rules: The only movement allowed is to tip the die from one square to an adjacent square. (You might think of the die as a large carton that is too heavy to slide to another square, but you can tip it over on an edge and have it land on an adjacent square.) Diagonal moves are, of course, not possible. And there's one more restriction. The number on top of the die must be the same as the number on the square you are moving to. A square with a skull and crossbones is a "wild" square. You can move to one of these squares no matter what number is on top of the die.

Jack the Hook became mightily confused and could not find a way back onto the center square. Can you solve this maze? To do so, you'll need your own personal lucky die, which you can probably find in one of the board games around the house. Here's an example to show how the die can be moved: At the start the only possible move is to go right, onto the square with the six. When we tip the die onto that square, a two will appear on top. We can now move up to a square with a two or right to a square with two. Suppose we go right. A one is now on top, and we could go right or down to a square with a one or up to a wild square. Let's suppose we go down, then right, then down. A six is now on top and no square with a six is next to the die. This is, therefore, a dead end and we would have to start over.

The terrible Captain Long John Silver and his pirates captured a small merchant ship containing several passengers, among them a beautiful woman named Julia. Captain Silver fell in love with her, but she refused to have anything to do with him. Finally, he offered her a deal: if she could solve one of his infamous dice mazes, she could go free; but if she failed, she must agree to become his wife. Julia had heard about the maze Captain Silver had used to defeat Jack the Hook, but she agreed to the deal.

In Silver's new maze, the die must again be tipped from square to square. The die starts on the red square, and it is positioned so that the two is on the top and the six faces the bottom of the maze. The object is to move the die off its starting square, then find a way to move it back onto that square.

Instead of numbers, Silver has drawn the letters L, H, O, and E in the squares. These stand for low, high, odd, and even. If a one, two, or three is on top of the die, you are allowed to tip the die onto a square with an L. If a four, five, or six is on top, you can tip the die onto an H. If a one, three, or five is on top, you can tip the die onto a square

with an O. If a two, four, or six is on top, you can tip the die onto an E.

Julia solved the maze with some secret help from Jack the Hook, who was still smarting from his defeat by Silver. Julia was set free and later married Jack the Hook, who gave up his cut-throat ways to become a respected businessman in Mobile, Alabama. Today his and Julia's great-grandchildren are majority stockholders in Hook Enterprises. But the question is: what route did Julia take to solve the maze?

Our story so far: In Maze 7, Dastardly Dan had tried to sabotage Jumping Jim's act by restringing all his trampolines. But Dan's actions had the opposite effect. The audience was so delighted by Jim's leaping about trying to reach the goal, that his act became the most popular of the circus.

The circus owner decided to commission Dastardly Dan to create another, even harder maze for Jim to solve. Dan added more trampolines, restrung them, and painted large numbers on each to indicate how far Jim will move when he bounces off each trampoline. The painted numbers would allow the audience to study the maze and try to find a solution before Jim did.

Dan also added a new rule that Jim had to follow. Certain of the numbers were painted in red and enclosed in circles. When Jim begins his act, he can move only vertically or horizontally through the maze of trampolines; he cannot move diagonally. However, if he lands on a red number in a circle, he must then start moving only diagonally; now he can't move vertically or horizontally. Jim must continue moving diagonally until he again lands on a red number. He then switches back to moving vertically or horizontally. And he switches each time he lands on a red number.

Here's an example to show how that works. Jim begins on the 4 at the northwest corner of the maze. From there he might move south four squares to the red 3. Now he must start moving diagonally. He might go three squares northeast to a 4. On the next move he would continue moving diagonally. He could move four squares southeast to a red 1. That red number would cause him to switch back to moving only horizontally or vertically.

Can you find a route that would let Jim land on the trampoline marked GOAL?

START

4	2	(2)	4	4	(3)	4	(3)
3	5	3	4	2	3	5	(2)
4	3	2	(5)	2	2	5	2
7	1	4	4	4	2	2	3
(3)	2	2	4	2	5	2	5
2	(3)	2	4	4	2	5	(1)
6	2	2	(3)	2	5	6	3
1	(2)	5	4	4	2	(1)	**GOAL**

27

Alice in Mazeland

The Red Queen has put Alice in a dungeon, in a room with a large maze drawn on the floor. In her shrill voice, the Queen tells Alice:

"If you can solve my maze, you can go free; if you can't, then it's off with your head! Since it's *my* maze, you have to follow *my* rules. You start on the square at the upper left and you have to get to the square at the lower right. The arrows show the directions you are allowed to take when you leave a square. Now here's the tricky part: When you leave a square you must travel for exactly one stride. You're only a little girl; so at the start of the maze, a stride will only take you to the next square."

Alice looked at the maze and saw that each square with a red arrow had a piece of cake with EAT ME written on the top, and each square with a green arrow had a small bottle labeled DRINK ME. She remembered from her previous adventures that eating the cake would make her grow, and drinking from the bottle would make her shrink.

"Each time you land on a square with a red arrow, you must eat a piece of the cake, which will make you grow and increase the length of your stride by one. Each time you land on a square with a green arrow, you must take a sip from the bottle, which will cause you to shrink and decrease the length of your stride by one. If you shrink too much, then you won't be able to move at all!"

"What a frightful way to end," said Alice. "I'll have to study this for quite a while before I begin."

Can you find a path that Alice can take from the starting square to the goal? Here is an example that shows how we can move through the maze. We begin on a square with an arrow that points east and south. Let's say we choose south and move one square in that direction. We land on a red arrow and add one to our stride. The red arrow points in only one direction; so on the next move we have no choice but to go south-east exactly two squares (since our stride is now two). We're now on a square with an arrow that points east; so we go two squares to the east. (By the way, whenever you travel for two or more squares, you should ignore the arrows on the square you pass over.) Now we're on a square with an arrow that points north and south. Let's choose to move north two squares, and next we must move east two squares. We're now on another square with an arrow that points north and south. We can't go north two squares, because that would take us outside the maze; so we move south two squares. This brings us to a square with a green arrow, and we subtract one from our stride, bringing the distance we move back to one. Just so we can end this example, let's pretend that we're really stupid and we move north-west from the green arrow, then south-east back onto the green arrow. Again we subtract one from our stride, which brings it down to zero. This means we can't move and have reached a dead end.

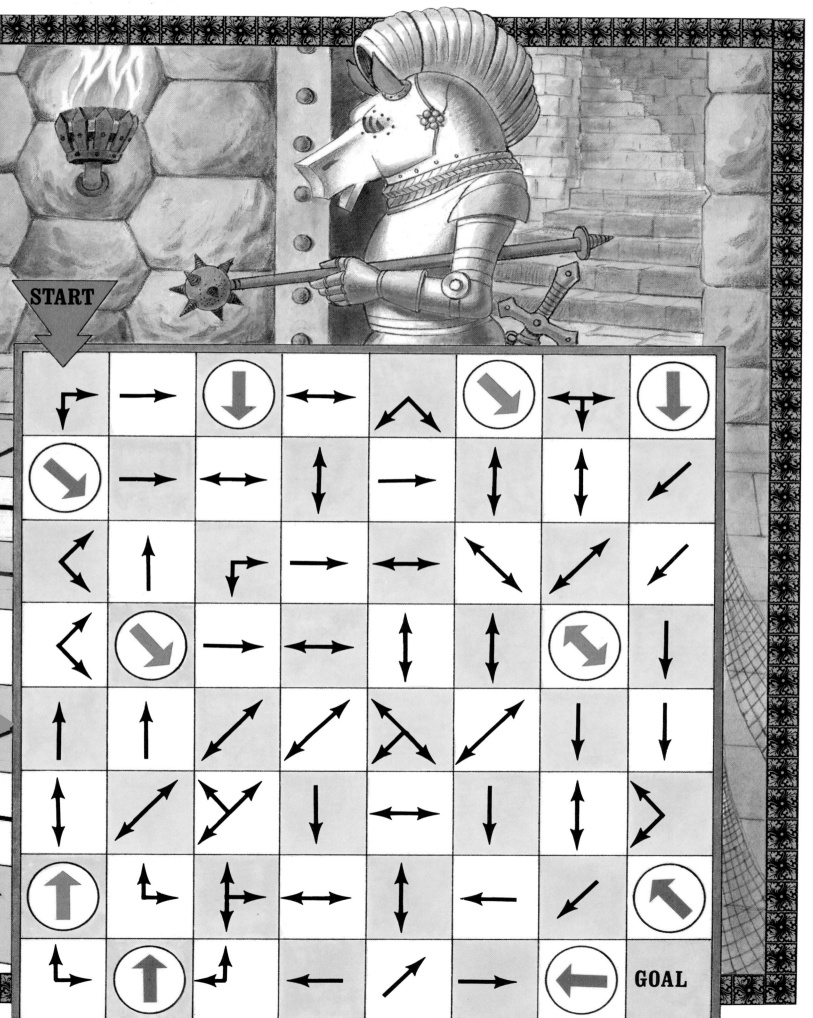

START

GOAL

MAD MAZE 17

THE THIRTEENTH LABOR OF HERCULES

(stone tablet in illustration)

1. Go horizontally to the same symbol or same color.
2. Go diagonally to the same symbol.
3. Go vertically to the same symbol or to the color.
4. Go diagonally to the same color.
5. Go to any other square that has both the symbol *and* the same color.
6. Are you on a corner square? If you are again with #1 on this tablet. If no, proceed to
7. There are two diagonal rows running thro square you are on. Is one diagonal row shor the other? If it is, proceed to #8. If it isn't again with #1.
8. Go to any square on the *shorter* diagon Then go to #2.

One fine day on Mt. Olympus, Hercules was complaining aloud to himself about the end of his latest romance. Unfortunately for him, Aphrodite the love goddess overheard his disparaging comments on the fickle nature of women; she decided to teach Hercules a lesson. She disguised herself as Hercules's most recent lost love, and called to him from the center of an enchanted meadow.

Hercules, hearing the voice, sped to the meadow and unwittingly entered the maze Aphrodite had prepared for him. Then Aphrodite taunted him. "Women are not fickle, Hercules," she said; "they simply change their minds in sensible ways. To teach you this, I have trapped you in a maze where the rules change with each step. However, there is logic to it all, and if you come to understand my rules, you will be freed and I will bless your next romance." With that

she pronounced a magical incantation; a cloud of smoke billowed forth, and when it cleared a huge stone tablet was standing in the meadow for Hercules to read. What the tablet said is shown in the box at the right.

Hercules begins the maze on the upper left square and he must first follow rule #1. That rule says to move horizontally to the same symbol or the same color. Since he starts on a red star, he could move right two squares to a red symbol or right four squares to a star. After completing that move, he then follows rule #2, and after each rule he advances to the next rule (unless, of course, the current rule says to do otherwise).

To be freed, Hercules must advance to the goal, which is the square at the bottom right. Can you find a path that will take him there? To solve the maze, you might take a pencil in each hand,

using the left-hand pencil to point to the current rule and right-hand pencil to travel through the maze.

1. Go horizontally to the same symbol or to the same color.
2. Go diagonally to the same symbol.
3. Go vertically to the same symbol or to the same color.
4. Go diagonally to the same color.
5. Go to any other square that has both the same symbol *and* the same color.
6. Are you on a corner square? If you are, begin again with #1 on this tablet. If no, proceed to #7.
7. There are two diagonal rows running through the square you are on. Is one diagonal row shorter than the other? If it is, proceed to #8. If it isn't, begin again with #1.
8. Go to any square on the *shorter* diagonal row. Then go to #2.

SPACEWRECK!

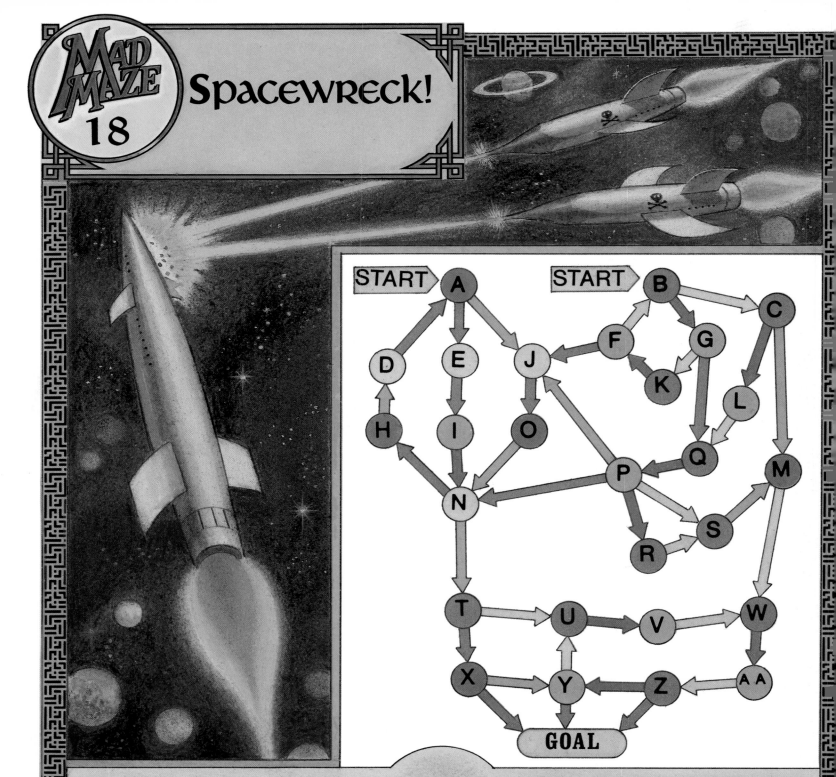

GOAL

The S.S. Fearless was on a routine spaceflight when it was attacked by space pirates. In a fierce battle, Captain Rocket and Lieutenant Lucky defeated the pirates, but their ship's Master Computer was damaged in the fight. Rocket is trapped in room A and Lucky trapped in room B. They cannot leave their rooms to enter the adjacent corridors because the life support system (normally controlled by the Master Computer) is now inoperative.

Lucky has a brilliant idea: use the manual override in each room to temporarily activate the corridor's life support system. Each room can activate the life support in any corridor of the same color. However, an operator must remain in the room while

the corridor is being used. Each corridor is constructed for travel in only one direction, so whoever walks through a corridor must travel in the direction of the arrow. If either Rocket or Lucky can make it to the Master Computer, he can repair it; otherwise, they both will remain lost in space. How can one of them get to the Master Computer—at the point marked "Goal" on the maze?

Here's an example to show how they can move through the spaceship. Since Captain Rocket starts in a purple room, he could operate the controls to enable Lucky to travel along the purple corridor from room B to room G. Lucky would now be in a green room and he could operate the controls to let Rocket travel through the green

corridor from room A to room J. Lucky could next move to K; Rocket could move to O; and Lucky could move to F. With Lucky now in a green room, Rocket could move down the green corridor to N; then he could make another move along the green corridor to T. (Note that you don't always have to alternate between Rocket and Lucky.) Captain Rocket is now getting close to the Master Computer and things are looking hopeful. But, alas, if you continue with this example you'll find that both space travelers will soon be trapped in endless loops. Whenever that happens, you'll just have to start over.

MAD MAZE 19

METEOR STORM!

START A
START B

With the insurance money from the wreck of their last spaceship (see the previous maze), Captain Rocket and Lieutenant Lucky have purchased a new ship, the S.S. Relatively Cautious. However, due to a navigational error, they jumped out of hyperspace and into the middle of a meteor storm. Once again, their ship was damaged badly, and the two hapless heroes found themselves, in a coincidence too remarkable to believe, trapped separately in compartments A and B, with the automatic life support system out of commission in every corridor. In order to survive, the pair must use the same strategy as last time to reach the Master Computer, at the circle marked GOAL. The new ship has a completely different floor plan, and it is an improved model that allows you to move either direction through a corridor.

Can you help the unlucky space travelers cheat death a second time?

Theseus and the Minotaur

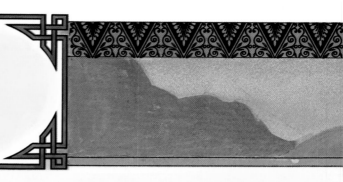

Theseus Popalopos applied for a research position with Minos Incorporated, an artificial intelligence firm in Palo Alto, California. He was interviewed by Ariadne Adams, leader of Project Minotaur, the project Theseus hoped to work on.

"As you know," Ariadne explained to him, "we are working on the creation of intelligent robots that we have been calling 'Minotaurs.' We are impressed by your résumé, but we would like you to come back tomorrow to take an aptitude test. The test is one of our own devising, and it is very difficult, but if you pass it we will hire you."

Theseus said that he would be happy to come back tomorrow; so Ariadne continued with her explanation. "Our test is simply this: you will be placed in a labyrinth we have constructed, and if you can find your way to the exit and leave the labyrinth, you will have passed the test. Here is a map of the labyrinth. You will start at the point I have marked with a T, which of course stands for 'Theseus.'" Ariadne's map is shown on the opposite page.

Theseus looked at the map and remarked that the labyrinth seemed to be very simple. "Wait," said Ariadne, "there's more to it. One of our prototype Minotaurs will also be placed in the maze at the point I'll mark here with an M. If the Minotaur can catch you before you reach the exit, then you flunk the test. The Minotaur has an excellent sensing system; so it will always know where you are. Its method of movement is also quite advanced: it will travel exactly twice as fast as you."

"That doesn't sound so good," said

Theseus. "How could anyone escape the Minotaur?"

"Well," said Ariadne, "the Minotaur has one flaw: its decision-making process is rather rudimentary. Here is a narrative description of the computer program that controls the Minotaur's decisions." Ariadne gave Theseus the list titled *Program for One Turn by the Minotaur.* "If you study the labyrinth, and study the way the Minotaur moves, you may be able to figure out how you can get to the exit. We'll see how you do tomorrow."

So—if you were Theseus, could you find your way through this labyrinth? What you have to do is take one turn for Theseus, moving him one square vertically or horizontally. (Of course, neither Theseus nor the Minotaur can move through any of the walls.) Then take *two* turns for the Minotaur, going twice through the Minotaur's program. This will result in the Minotaur moving zero, one, or two squares.

Here's an example. Suppose Theseus is at the point marked *T1* in the diagram below and the Minotaur is at *M1*. You might move Theseus to *T2*. You would then go twice through the Minotaur's program, causing the Minotaur to move to *M2*. If Theseus is next moved to *T3*, then the Minotaur would move to *M3*; and if Theseus is moved to *T4*, then the Minotaur would move to *M4*. The Minotaur has now caught Theseus; so Theseus would have flunked the test.

That example makes the Minotaur look pretty powerful, but consider this example. Suppose Theseus is at *T5* and the Minotaur at *M5*. If Theseus moves to *T6*, the Minotaur would move to *M6*.

Now, suppose Theseus moves to *T7*. To us humans, it would appear that the best move for the Minotaur would be to move south, then east to capture Theseus. But the Minotaur doesn't think that way. If you strictly follow the program for the Minotaur, you'll find that he would move to *M7*. Theseus could continue to *T8* and the Minotaur would move to *M8*; then Theseus could move to *T9* and the Minotaur to *M9*. Finally Theseus could move to *T10* and the Minotaur would make no move. Theseus could then continue out of the labyrinth.

There's one additional rule: at any point you can let Theseus pause—that is, make no move. You would then simply make two more passes through the Minotaur's program.

Probably the best way to work on this maze is to use a pencil in one hand to follow Theseus's moves through the maze and use a pencil in your other hand to follow the Minotaur's. After you get used to the way the Minotaur moves, you'll probably want to skip reading through its program. That's okay, but just be sure not to move the Minotaur vertically when it's possible to move it horizontally. There's basically only one solution to the maze, but at some points there are alternate routes that Theseus could take. The solution involves between ninety and one hundred moves on the part of Theseus.

This is the hardest maze in the book; in fact it's possible that no one will solve it. But it's still a lot of fun just to wander through the maze—to step from behind a wall, arouse the Minotaur, then see him charge mindlessly towards you.

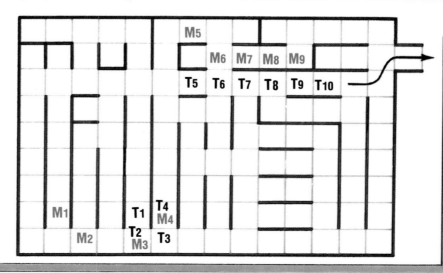

Program for One Turn by the Minotaur

Step 1. Can the Minotaur move horizontally and get closer to Theseus? If *Yes*, go to Step 2. If *No*, go to Step 3.

Step 2. Move horizontally one square towards Theseus. Then go to Step 5.

Step 3. Can the Minotaur move vertically and get closer to Theseus? If *Yes*, go to Step 4. If *No*, go to Step 5.

Step 4. Move vertically one square toward Theseus. Then go to Step 5.

Step 5. End of turn.

HINTS:

Hint for Maze 1:
The Arctic Caves of Norway

This is the easiest maze in the book, but it does have an interesting complication. To solve the maze, you have to go through some passageways that look like they lead nowhere. If you just wander around the maze, you should come across the mysterious passageways needed for the solution. But if you just concentrate on paths that lead to the exit, you may never find the way out.

Hint for Maze 2:
Road Rally

At two separate points in this maze, the true path doubles back on itself. So if you think you're retracing your steps, you may not really be retracing your steps. Having the true path double back is a basic trick of mine that I use in many of these mazes.

Hint for Maze 3:
The Farmer Goes to Market

I can explain this maze better if I refer to the upper-right quadrant of town as the Confusing Quarter (an area of picturesque streets and local color, somewhat like the French Quarter in New Orleans). When you start the maze you travel through three intersections and you've entered the Confusing Quarter. You might wander around here for a while until you discover that there's only one way out: the north-south road that runs through the center of the Confusing Quarter. This road will take you to the bottom of the maze. You are then forced to turn east and then north up the road at the right side of the maze. Unfortunately, this road takes you back into the Confusing Quarter. At that point (if everything goes as I planned) you will despair, thinking that you've been here before. But that's the trick. It's true that you've been to this section of the maze before, but you're entering the section from a different point. If you make the correct turns, you'll find that you can now reach a new exit from the Confusing Quarter. And if you find that new exit, you'll be about 40% of the way to the goal.

Hint for Maze 4:
The Itsy Bitsy Spider

There's nothing really tricky about this maze; the only difficulty is that, at first, it's a little hard to visualize how to move through it. Once you've become adept at moving through the maze, you might watch out for some long false paths. They don't stop at dead ends, but instead they go around in loops. Actually, I think some of these false paths are more interesting than the true path to the goal.

Hint for Maze 5:
The Spider's Web

All the false paths in this maze lead to dead ends. Knowing that, it should be possible to get through the maze if you keep track of the points where the paths diverge and you have to make a choice. If you choose a path that

---

goes to a dead end, just go back to the last choice point and choose a different path (and if all paths from that point lead to dead ends, then go to the *previous* choice point).

Here is an interesting mechanical method you could use to solve this maze. It's rather magical because it gets you to the goal without you having to keep any information about where you've been. Use a pencil (or any kind of pointer) to move through the maze. When you reach a bug where you have to make a choice, do the following: Start at the line you used to reach the bug and move your pencil around the bug in a *clockwise* manner. When you reach another line, exit along that line. When you reach a dead end, simply turn around and go back on the path you used to enter the dead end.

If you follow that method you would arrive at Bug A as your first choice point. If you think of the bug as the center of a clock, you reached it from the direction of nine o'clock. If you go around Bug A in a clockwise direction you would reach a line that exits in the direction of three o'clock, towards Bug B. You would travel along that line and quickly come to a dead end. You'd then turn around, move back, and arrive back at Bug A (this time coming from the direction of three o'clock). Again you move clockwise around Bug A, and now you will leave on the line that heads in the direction of six o'clock, toward Bug C. And so forth.

This method is similar to the "right-hand-rule" or the "left-hand-rule" used to thread conventional mazes. If you think these mechanical methods (or algorithms) are fun (actually, most people don't think they're fun), then you might go through the maze again using the same method, except this time choose the first path in the *counter-clockwise* direction. This will also get you to the goal, but it will take you through different parts of the maze.

Hint for Maze 6:
No Left Turns! No Right Turns!

Phil's town is divided into two sections, connected by a bridge. Obviously, the first thing you have to do is leave Phil's house in the right section of town and go over to the left section. That isn't too difficult; so I'll assume you've gotten that far and are now wandering around the left section trying to get to Carl's Auto Repair. Since both Carl's Auto Repair and the power station are in the left section of town, there's obviously no reason to go back to the right section. That's a safe assumption to make, isn't it? If it is, then the best strategy is just to keep going around the left section until you find a way to Carl's Auto Repair.

Hint for Maze 7:
Jumping Jim

In the hint for Maze 5, I described a mechanical method (or algorithm) that could be used to solve that maze. That particular method would not work here, because the false paths in Maze 7 do not stop at dead ends. The false paths here all end in loops. Actually, they're worse than loops: they're a confused mess of squares that lead to each other but don't lead to any way out.

Bob Wittrock (I mentioned him in the Introduction) showed me an amusing algorithm that can be used to solve Maze 7. I thought I would pass it on, though you probably won't want to get into this unless you're one of the few people who think algorithms are a lot of fun. I'll call Wittrock's method the "Sequenced Bread Crumb Algorithm," after the bread crumbs that Hansel and Gretel tried to use to mark their path through the woods. Instead of bread crumbs, you'll need some stickers cut into tiny little squares. Post-Its are good to use here because you can easily remove them after you've solved the maze. Use just the sticky part of the Post-It and cut it into little squares.

Start by placing a sticker (that is, the small, cut-up part of a sticker) on the starting square of the maze. Use a pencil to label that sticker A. Choose any square you can move to from that starting square and put a sticker on that square. Label that sticker B. Make any move from B to a square that you will put a sticker on labeled C. Continue in this fashion, but never make a move that would take you to a square that already has a sticker on it. Eventually you'll get to a square where you can't move any further. Suppose you just labeled that square H. Draw a line through the H, then go back to the last square, the one you labeled G. Now make a different move from G. If you can't move from G, cross out the letter G and go back to the square labeled F. Suppose you can make a move from F. You would put a sticker on the square you moved to, and you'd label that sticker G (because the other G has been crossed out). As you continue with this method, some of the false paths of the maze will be marked by stickers with crossed-out letters, and eventually the method will lead you to the goal.

Hint for Maze 8:
Apollo and Diana

The "Sequenced Bread Crumb Algorithm" described in the hint for Maze 7 also works for this maze.

Hint for Maze 9:
Apollo's Revenge

By now you're probably aware of my trick of having the true path double back on itself. I use that trick to excess here. After several moves the true path gets to the column that's fifth from the left of the grid. It then travels down that column, goes up the column, and comes back down. It then leaves the column, only to come back to go up once more, then down once more. I figured that was the maximum number of double-backs I could get under the rules for this maze. By the way, the "Sequenced Bread Crumb Algorithm," which worked so well in Mazes 7 and 8, does not work here. The reason, of course, is that the true path in Maze 9 can land on a single square two different times—once in the following-the-arrow-head state and once in the following-the-arrow-tail state. The algorithm could be modified to handle two states (you could use stickers of two colors, or you could put the stickers in two different sections of the squares), but whatever

---

you try is apt to get pretty confusing and un-wieldy.

Hint for Maze 10:
Grandpa's Transit Map

Here is some help to get you past the first part of the solution. At the first village you come to after Startsburg, transfer to the blue cable car going west. Next, find a loop that will allow you to get turned around and take the blue cable car back to that first village. Then transfer to the blue trolley car going east. You'll now be about a quarter of the way to the goal.

Hint for Maze 11:
Tarzan and Jojo

In Maze 6 I tried to fool you into thinking that once you got from the right to the left section of town, there was no point in going back to the right section. Did you fall for that? If you did, you probably can't be fooled again. So you no doubt realize that once you get from the upper section of Maze 11 to the lower section, then you'll probably have to go back to the upper section and come back down again. That is true, but there are other complications. There are actually seven separate paths that connect the upper and lower sections. You have to find the correct path down, the correct path back up, then the correct path down again.

By the way, if you enjoyed the "Sequenced Bread Crumb Algorithm" that's described in the hint for Maze 7, then you'll be happy to know that it also works for this maze.

Hint for Maze 12:
Grand Master of the Road Rally

This maze has certain similarities to Maze 1. In that maze you could be in one of two states, depending on whether you just went through a hot or a cold area. In Maze 12 you can be in one of four states, depending on whether you just went through an A, a B, a C, or a D. Doubling the number of states didn't just double the complexity of this maze. I'd estimate that Maze 12 is ten to twenty times as complex as Maze 1.

The solution to Maze 1 involved traveling through a loop that looked like it didn't lead anywhere. What happened in that loop is that you changed states (from cold to hot). Maze 12 has a similar solution. At the bottom of the map there are streets that look like they're part of a separate suburb. I'll call this suburb "Abeeceeville," since there's an A, a B, and a C on the streets.

The solution involves traveling down the left-hand road from Loydsville to Abeeceeville, looping through Abeeceeville, then returning by the same road to Loydsville. You're now almost a quarter of the way to the goal. Before you read the next paragraph you might want to return to the maze to see if you can go the rest of the way to the goal. But I should warn you that there is more tricky business ahead.

What is really tricky about this maze is that after more travel through Loydsville, you make a *second* trip down to Abeeceeville. This time you're in a different state (you just went through a D). Again, you travel down the left-hand road, loop through Abeeceeville, then return by the same road to Loydsville. Incidentally, the right-hand road from Abeeceeville is not used. It's just there to fool you into thinking the solution involves going *through* Abeeceeville.

Hint for Maze 13:
Pirates and Plunder
If you've been working through these mazes in numeric order, you've now gotten to the really complex mazes in the book. In Maze 12, you could be at the same spot on the map and be in one of four different states (depending on what letter you just went through). In Maze 13 you can be on the same square of the diagram and be in one of *twenty-four* different states. That's because the die can be put on a square in twenty-four different ways: six different numbers could be on top and, for each of those six numbers, four different numbers can be facing you.

In any of these multi-state mazes it's difficult to keep track of where you are if you just look at the maze itself. You can, however, always resort to making a separate diagram to map your way through the maze. The trick here is to work out a good notation system. One simple system that would work with Maze 13 is shown in figure 1 below.

The top line of the diagram is the dead-end path that I used as an example in the explanation of the maze. The letters stand for map directions. The arrows pointing up or down are other paths that branch off from the path. I filled in one of these branches. If you continue with this diagram, filling in the various paths, you should eventually find one that leads to the goal. You might get stuck in a loop, but your diagram should help you recognize that.

This notation system could probably be improved on. You might, for instance, want to keep track of the current state of the die (if you do, you should record not just the number on top but also the number facing you). If you have some graph paper, you might mark out a grid of 7 x 7 fairly large squares. You could then draw paths on the grid (and on your paths you might note the current state of the die). I used a method similar to this when I constructed the maze, and I needed three separate grids to fit in the entire map of the maze.

Hint for Maze 14:
Damsel in Distress!
This maze starts out pretty easy. You're on a narrow path and you don't have to make any choices for the first seven moves. Then you reach a section that's something of a wilderness. It's the 3 x 3 grid of squares with the letters HEL-OOL-HLL. There is a high density of false paths here and it's hard to find your way around. If you can get out of that wilderness, where you want to go is up the vertical column that's near the center of the maze (it's the column with the letters O-H-H-O-H, reading from top down). If you can

get to the O at the top of the column, and if you are on the true path, then a two will be on top of the die and a four will be facing you. (There's one other way to get to that square, but it's a false path that ends at that square.) If you start traveling left from the O, you can make twelve moves that will take you around a loop and back to the O. You might think that you're stuck in a loop, because you've been here before. But notice that you're now in a different state: a four is now on top of the die and a six faces you. So that loop might be on the true path to the goal. Or maybe not. But I've already given too many hints for this maze; so I'd better stop here.

Hint for Maze 15:
Jumping Jim's Encore
The solution to this maze has a tricky start; so I'll give you the first five moves. The first move is south four squares to the red 3. You now switch to moving diagonally, and the next moves are south-east, north-east, north-west, south-west. You're now back at that red 3, and you switch back to moving vertically or horizontally.

The true path to the goal is not long, but the maze is still very difficult. Once you start down a false path, you can travel through a vast territory before you realize that you're retracing your steps.

Hint for Maze 16:
Alice in Mazeland
Here's how the solution to the maze begins: The first move is south one square to a square with a red arrow. When you leave the red arrow, you will be traveling two squares on each move. Then, before you land on any green arrow or on any other red arrow, you should find a way back to the first red arrow you visited. Again you leave that square, and you're now traveling three squares on each move. At this point you'll be about 15% of the way to the goal.

Hint for Maze 17:
The Thirteenth Labor of Hercules
In the hint to Maze 13 I discussed making separate diagrams as a way of mapping the various routes you could take through a maze. That method would work for Maze 17; in fact, it may be the only method that will work for this maze. Without some sort of a map, it's very difficult to keep track of where you have been in this maze.

If you plan to draw a map of the paths you explore in the maze, you will, of course, need some sort of notation system. You can develop your own system, or you might consider using a system that I worked out. I used my system to draw a complete map of the maze—one that shows every path that can be reached from the start of the maze. This map is printed in the section of the book that gives the

solution for this maze. If you use my notation when you draw your map, then later on you can compare your map with mine. Our maps will not look the same, but you will be able to see how they relate to each other.

My notation system uses a three-digit number to describe where you are. The first two digits are the square you are on, and I numbered the squares like this:

11	12	13	14	15
21	22	23	24	25
31	32	33	34	35
41	42	43	44	45
51	52	53	54	55

The third digit is the number of the rule you will follow for the next move.

Figure 2 below gives an example. The top row shows a path that goes from the start to a dead end. Branching off from the top row are other paths that are only partially diagrammed. One of these paths, if diagrammed far enough, will get you to the goal. Note that the starting state is 111, meaning you are on the upper-left square and will follow rule number 1. From the starting state you can get to the state numbered 152 or to the state numbered 132. 152 means that you're on the green star at the upper right of the diagram and you will next follow rule 2. 132 means you are on the red circle on the top row of the diagram and you will also next follow rule 2.

Hint for Maze 18:
Spacewreck!
This maze has an abundance of loopiness. If you use a pencil in one hand to follow the moves of Captain Rocket, and a pencil in the other hand to follow Lieutenant Lucky, you'll reach a lot of points where one hand is going around one endless loop and the other hand is going around another endless loop.

The solution to the maze is also pretty loopy. The solution starts with your right hand going around the loop B-G-K-F-B while your left hand goes around the loop A-J-O-N-H-D-A. After your right hand has gone around its loop once or twice you might think that you are retracing your steps. But you don't really start retracing your steps until your right hand has gone around its loop three times, and your left hand has completed two trips around its loop. There are several paths you can take to escape from those dual loops. Only one of those paths will lead to the goal.

Hint for Maze 19:
Meteor Storm!
In the Introduction, I implored the reader not to give up too soon on any maze. Well—I take that back. With Maze 19, the best course of action is probably to give up right now . . . unless the maze really has you fascinated.

Maze 19 is interesting, because the layout looks simple but the solution is complex. Unfortunately, the solution is so hugely complex that you could spend weeks going around in the maze. In the solution section, I present a map that shows all the paths through the maze. That map gives a good indication of the complexity of this maze.

The maze has several routes to the goal. The shortest route will get you there in forty moves.

By the way, I estimate that Maze 20 is probably more complex than this maze, but I can still recommend spending a month or two with that maze before reading its hint or solution. Maze 20 is more varied and has more interesting situations for you to get into.

Hint for Maze 20:
Theseus and the Minotaur
Here are the first eight moves of the solution: nN - nNW - eWW - eWW - eWW - sWW- sWS - wW. Theseus' moves are shown as small letters and the Minotaur's moves as capital letters. Theseus' first move is to go north one square; then the Minotaur goes north one square. Theseus' next move is again to go north one square; and the Minotaur goes north one square then west one square, and so on.

At the end of those moves, the Minotaur is trapped in what I thought of as a cup: a square that's open on only one side. Theseus is on the square directly below that cup, and he is free to move down the column he's on without being pursued by the Minotaur. The key to solving this maze is to lure the Minotaur into similar traps in different parts of the labyrinth.

The next trap is fairly simple. After moving to the bottom row, Theseus goes three squares east; then he ducks behind a wall. Theseus will be on the east side of the wall and the Minotaur is trapped on the west side.

At this point you're in the most complex part of the maze. There are many false paths you could take from here that go towards the exit, but they don't quite make it to the exit before the Minotaur grabs you. What you have to do is lure the Minotaur into another trap. The location of that trap is not at all obvious. I'll tell you where it is in the next paragraph, but before you read that paragraph you might want to return to the maze to see if you can get any further.

The next trap is the cup that's right next to the exit. This cup is made up of two squares. You may not have thought of that trap, since it's impossible for you to leave the labyrinth if the Minotaur is sitting in that cup. But that trap lets you lead the Minotaur into subsequent traps.

Figure 1

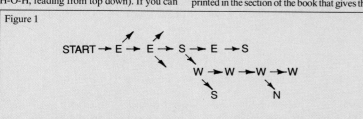

Figure 2

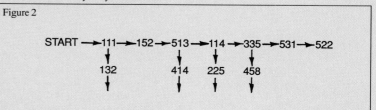

SOLUTIONS:

Solution to Maze 1:
The Arctic Caves of Norway
At the bottom of the maze, in the middle, there is a vertical pathway that goes up to a small loop—the loop with two red areas and one blue area. That loop is cleverly designed to look like it doesn't lead anywhere, but only by traveling through it can you reach the goal.

To solve the maze, take any route that will get you to the loop, go around the loop, then take any of several routes that will get you from there to the goal.

Solution to Maze 2:
Road Rally
Here's the path from START to GOAL. At each intersection move in the following directions. (In this solution, and in most of the solutions in the book, I think of the maze as a map and I indicate the directions as you would for a map.)

E-E-E-E-E-S (we've just gone around the upper-right corner of the maze) S-S-S-W-NE-N-N-N-W (we just went around the upper-right corner again) W-S-SE-SW-E-S-W-W-W-N (we went around the lower-left corner) N-N-NE-W (we're now only a block from the start) S-S-S-S-E (we again went around the lower-left corner) E-E-E-E-S.

Solution to Maze 3:
The Farmer Goes to Market
What's tricky about this maze is that traveling in one direction on a block is entirely different from traveling in the other direction on that same block. That basic element of confusion allowed me to put some disorienting features in the maze. At several points the true path doubles back on itself. In the upper-right quadrant (the area I called the "Confusing Quarter" in the hint for this maze) I hoped to lead you into a few false paths. Then later, if you find the true path, you travel back over some of those false paths but in the opposite direction.

The shortest path from start to finish is shown below. At each successive intersection take the direction indicated by the letter. Corners are considered to be intersections, and I thought it would be helpful to add an asterisk when you've just gone around a corner.

E-E-E-S-S-S-E-N*-N-N-N-W*-W-S-S-E-E-S-S-W*-W-W-N-N-N-W-S*-S-S-E*- E-N-W-W-N-N-E*-S-S-E-E-E-E.

This is the first maze I ever constructed. It appeared in Martin Gardner's Mathematical Games column in the October 1962 *Scientific American*. When the maze first appeared it had these same rules and the same story, but the layout was different. After 28 years I found I could improve the layout.

Incidentally, the story that accompanied the maze contained a veiled reference to a feud that was going on in 1962 between the great Henry Barns, who was New York's traffic commissioner, and Robert Moses, who built the expressways in New York State. The reference was, no doubt, too veiled for anyone to notice, and now, of course, the whole affair is long forgotten.

Solution to Maze 4:
The Itsy Bitsy Spider
The list below shows the moves to make to get from the south-east corner of Level E to the north-west corner of Level A. ("South-east" and "north-west" make sense if you think of the diagram of each level as a map.) N, S, E, and W are the directions north, south, east, and west. These are used when you travel from room to room on the same level. U means up (you go from the room on a level to the corresponding room on the level above) and D means down. The numbers in parentheses refer to the notes below.

W-U-N-N-D(1)-S-E-U-S-U-W-W-N-D-W-D-N-U-U-S-U-E-U-E-D-N-U-W-D(2)- N-U-W

(1) I hope that the first time you tried this maze you made the mistake of moving N or U at this point. These directions lead to the more interesting false paths of the maze.

(2) An alternate path from this point is W-U-N.

Solution to Maze 5:
The Spider's Web
The moves listed here show the route to the goal. The letters show the direction of each 3-bug move. The numbers in parentheses refer to the notes below.

E-SW-S-S-SE-W-N(1)-N-E(2)-E-E-S-S-W-W-N-N-E(3)-E-SW-E-SW-NW-NW-S-S-E-E-NW-NW-E(4)-E-E-S-W-SW-E-NW-NW-S-S

(1) I thought that maneuver might confuse you—did it? It looks like you're turning around and retracing your path.

(2) This is the first time you travel east along the line at the middle of the maze.

(3) This is the second time you travel east along the middle line.

(4) This is the third time you travel east along the middle line. By this time, I figured you might think you'd already taken this route before.

Solution to Maze 6:
No Left Turns! No Right Turns!
You start this maze at Phil's house in the right section of town. The first thing you have to do is get across the bridge to the left section of town. This can be done by making the following moves at each intersection (the letters stand for straight, right, or left, and corners are considered to be intersections):

S-S-S-S-R-R (around a corner) R-S-R-R-R-S-S-R-S-R (around a corner) S-R-S-R-S-R-R-S-R-S-R-R-S-S-S.

You're now heading across the bridge to the left section of town. When you're in the left section, take *any* route to the power station and go down the block with the jagged red line (you can go down that block in either direction). You've now switched to the straight-or-left-only state. Now take any route back to the *right* section of town. After reaching the right section, get yourself turned around and head back to the left section of town (that should be easy). After crossing the bridge to the left section, make these moves at each intersection:S-L-S-S-S-L-L-L (the last three moves took you around a loop) S- S-S.

You then go through the jagged red line again and switch back to the straight-or-right-only state. Then make two right turns and you're at Carl's Auto Repair.

What's really clever about this maze is that by dividing the town into two sections I thought I could get you to make an unconscious assumption that once you get from the right section to the left section there is no point in going back to the right section. You might think that my discussion of this maze in the Hints section was unfair, since I seem to encourage that assumption. But I thought that by making the assumption explicit, there would be a better chance of it being re-examined.

Solution to Maze 7:
Jumping Jim
This grid has all the numbers of the maze. To show the shortest path to the goal, I added letters to indicate the direction of each move. You start on the number at the upper left and move three squares east, then you move three squares south, and so forth. (There are other notations in the grid that I use later to explain more about the maze.)

3E	6S	-4-	3S	-2-	4W	3
2	1	2	3S	2	(5)	2
-2E-	3	-4E-	3S	-4W-	(2)	-3W-
2	(4)	4	3S	4	(2)	2
-4E-	-5-	-1-	3W	-2N-	5	-4-
4	3	-2-	2E	4	5N	6
-2-	5E	-2-	5N	-6-	(1)	Goal

I thought it would be interesting to explain how the maze works. You begin in a network of numbers that are underlined in the diagram. All of the underlined numbers—except for one—lead to other underlined numbers. The idea here was to get you to circle aimlessly around this network.

One underlined number leads to a network of numbers enclosed in hyphens. All these—except for one—lead to other numbers in hyphens or back to underlined numbers. One number in hyphens leads to a network of unmarked numbers. The unmarked numbers lead to other unmarked numbers or back to numbers that are enclosed in hyphens or are underlined. And finally, one unmarked number leads to the goal.

The numbers in parentheses provide false paths back from the goal. These are paths that could lead to the goal (or to the true path that leads to the goal), but you can't get to these false paths from the start of the maze. Most mazes should have some sort of confusion like this around the goal; otherwise it would be easy to solve the maze by starting at the goal and working backwards to the start. In this particular maze, I didn't have room for enough of these false paths; so working back from the goal (at least part of the way) would have been a good technique for solving this maze.

I'm afraid I have to report that the rules for this maze are not, as I first believed, an original idea of mine. In fact these rules first appeared almost a century ago in a puzzle by Sam Loyd. Loyd's puzzle was called "Back from the Klondike" and it was first published in his newspaper column in 1898. It involved a grid of 325 numbers and was extremely difficult to solve. It was presented as a contest in the newspaper.

If you want to follow up on that puzzle, you can find it in *Mathematical Puzzles of Sam Loyd*, edited by Martin Gardner. There's a further discussion of the puzzle in Gardner's book *Penrose Titles to Trapdoor Ciphers*. I especially recommend the last book because it also contains Gardner's discussion of my card game "The New Eleusis."

Solution to Maze 8:
Apollo and Diana
The following lists the 25 moves of the solution. Each move starts with one or two letters that show the direction of the move, followed by a number that shows the number of squares moved.

E2-S4-S2-SE1-NE3-NW3-E3-W5-S1-W1-N1-E7-SW1-W3-SE2-NE2-W5-SW1-SE4-N7-SW3-SW2-S2-NE7-S7

Solution to Maze 9:
Apollo's Revenge
You can get to the goal by the following 32 moves. Each move starts with one or two letters that show the direction of the move, followed by a number that shows the number of squares moved. An asterisk indicates a change from following heads to following tails (or vice versa).

E5-SW4-S1-S1-N5-S2-NE2-S4-*E3-N4-SW4 - SE1 - NE2 - NW1 - S1 - N3 - S1 - S3-NW2 - *E2 - N1 - N2 - S4 - S1 - SE1 - NW5-SE2 - *W2 - S3 - NE3 - NE3 - *S6

Solution to Maze 10:
Grandpa's Transit Map
Beginning at Startsburg, leave the villages in these directions: W-W (we now go around the upper-left corner of the map) S-S-S-S (and around the lower-left corner) N-N-W. The last five moves took us around a loop. We could also have gone around that loop in the opposite direction. We now retrace part of our path. N-N- N (and around the upper-left corner again) E-E-E (now around the upper-right corner) S-S-W-W-W-W-N-N-E; and we've arrived in Crumbsburg. SE-SW-S-S-W-W-NE-E-E-NE-SE-S-W. The next eleven moves will take us most of the way around a large circle. I wrote something about that circle in the paragraph below. N-N-N-N-NW-SW (we seem to be in Crumbsburg again) SW-SW-SE-SE-SE-E-S and we've reached Endenville.

The large circle I mentioned above is an interesting feature of this maze. You've probably already discovered that circle, because a lot of the false paths dump you there. The false paths enter in such a way that you're forced into an endless loop around the circle in the *clockwise* direction. The true path also enters the circle, but it goes around it in a *counter-clockwise* direction.

Solution to Maze 11:
Tarzan and Jojo
You'll notice that there's an upper and a lower section to this maze, and these two sections are joined by two narrow connec-

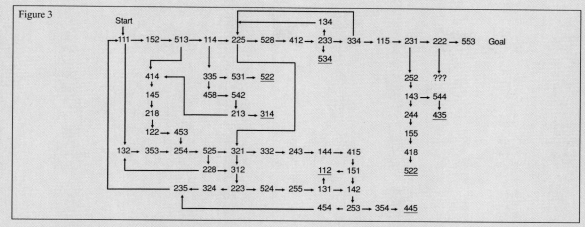

Figure 3

tors. After some experimenting I found that I could squeeze up to four separate maze paths in either of these connectors (two paths heading down and two paths heading up). I was therefore able to construct a pretty complicated maze (with four paths in the left connector but only three in the right connector).

The true path wiggles around the upper section for a while then goes down the connector on the left. It wiggles around the bottom section then heads back up the left connector. It then goes to the connector on the right, comes down, and goes to the goal. To make things really confusing, there's a false path coming down each connector and another false path going up each connector.

It takes 40 moves to get to the goal. Each move is shown as one or two letters that give the direction of the move and a number that indicates the distance moved.

S4-S3-E3-NE3-S4. (That last move was pretty tricky. S3 would have taken you on an interesting false path that goes down the right-side connector.) N3-NW3-E3-W4-W4-E3-SW3-S4-S4-S4-S3-E3-E3-N3-S4. (We're now on the square next to the goal.) N3-N3-W3-SW3-N4-N4-N4-N3-E4-E4-S3-S3-S3-S3-W4-E3-S4-W4-E3-S3.

Solution to Maze 12:
Grand Master of the Road Rally
In the hint for this maze I explain that the solution involves making two trips down to "Abeeceeville," the small suburb at the bottom of the map. Here is the complete solution. The capital letters represent the red letters traveled through. The small letters represent the direction (north, south, east, or west) you travel at each intersection.

A-s-e-B-e-C-s-w-D-w-A-w. At this point you take the road down to Abeeceeville, travel north on the street with the B, travel south on the street with the C, then return by the road you came down on. Back in Loydsville the solution continues as follows: s-D-e-A-e-B-e-(here comes a tricky loop around a block)-s-C-w-n-D-e-e-n-n-A-w-s-B-s-s-C-w-s-D-w-A-w-B-(then around the corner)-C-n-D-w. Now you take the second trip to Abeeceeville, travel north on the street with the A, then south on the street with the B, then back on the road you came down on. The rest of the solution is easy: n-C-n-e-D-n-A-e-e-B-s-C-e-D-e-e-A-Goal.

Solution to Maze 13:
Pirates and Plunder
It takes 48 moves to get back to the center square. The moves are shown below. For each move I show a number (that's the number on top of the die at the start of the move) and I show a letter (that indicates the direction of the move). For example, you start with a six on top and you move east. Now a two is on top and you again move east, and so forth.

6E-2E-1E-5N-4W-1N-2E-4S-1W-2W-6S-3S-1S-4E-2E-3N-1N-4N-6W-2W-1N-3N-6W-5W-1W-2S-3S-5S-4S-2S-3E-1E-4S-5W-1W-2N-4N-5N-3N-2W-6N-4N-1E-2S-4E-6E-3S-5S.

Rolling a die across a grid can be pretty strange—you're never sure what number will pop up next or how the die will be repositioned. Well—I'll take that back—you can know what number will pop up next, but I myself never fully understood what was happening to the die as it turned in different directions. So how, you might ask, did I create this maze? It was mostly just trial and error.

If you're interested in the topology of this problem you might look up some of Martin Gardner's *Scientific American* columns. In the December 1963 issue he presents a problem by Roland Sprague that involves rolling a set of alphabet blocks across a chessboard. In the November 1965 issue, and later in the March 1975 issue, he presents rolling cube problems by John Harris.

Solution to Maze 14:
Damsel in Distress!
It takes 66 moves to go through the maze. Each move is shown here as a number (the number on top of the die at the start of the move) and a letter (the direction of the move).

The solution starts with these moves: 2S-1E-4S-5S-3E-6E-4E-1N-5E-3S-1E-2N-3W-1W-4N-5N-3N. We are now at a point that I mentioned in the hint for this maze. We are on a square with an O, and the die has a two on top and a four facing us. Here are the next twelve moves: 2W-6N-4N-1E-2N-3E-6E-4S-2S-3W-6S-5W.

We've now gone around a loop and are back at the square with the O. I thought I could confuse you with some *deja vu* here. While it's true that we've been on this square before, we're now in a different *state*: a four

is on top of the die and a six faces us. The next twelve moves are these: 4W-2N-6N-5E-4N-1E-2E-6S-4S-1W-2S-3W. We've now made a *second* trip around the loop and (as Yogi Berra said) it's *deja vu* all over again. Now a six is on top of the die and a two faces us. At this point we start a *third* trip around the loop: 6W-4N-2N-3E-6N-5E-4E-2S. We finally leave the loop here and the route to the goal is fairly straightforward: 6E-3S-5S-4S-2S-3W-6W-4W-1S-5S-6W-3W-1W-4N-5N-3W-6N.

Solution to Maze 15:
Jumping Jim's Encore
You can reach the goal by these sixteen moves: 4S-3SE-4NE-3NW-4SW-3N-3E-4S-4E-1SW-6NW-4SE-2NE-5SW-2E-4E. The numbers indicate the distance moved; the letters indicate the direction.

Solution to Maze 16:
Alice in Mazeland
Here's the series of moves that will get you to the goal. Each move starts with a number that indicates the distance of the move, followed by one or two letters that indicate the direction of the move.

1S-2SE-2E-2S-2W-2NW-2NE-2W-3SE-3NE-3S-3S-4W-4N-4E-3NW-3W. (At this point we're back on the starting square.) 3S-3SE-3W-2N-2N-2NE-3S-3E-3N-3SE-2SW-2SW-2W-2N-2N-2N-2E-2E-1SE-1S-1SW-1S-1SW-1W-1S-1W-1S-1W-2N-2NE-2E-2S-2S-2E.

Solution to Maze 17:
The Thirteenth Labor of Hercules
Figure 3 is a map that shows not just the solution to this maze but also every path you can reach from the start of the maze (well, almost every path). To figure out this map you have to read the hint I gave for this maze.

The map shows the tangle created by the false paths as they join with each other. Some false paths go into a loop and others loop back to the start of the maze. Some false paths go to dead ends, and I've underlined the states on the map that are dead ends. There are a couple of false paths that I didn't have room to add to the map; they are represented by the arrow that points to three question marks. I figured that no one would take these paths because they branch off the true

path when it's only one move from the goal.

Constructing this maze was quite an experience. The first part was easy: I created the true path and a couple of interesting false paths, and this filled in about three-fourths of the squares. But filling in the remaining one-fourth was horribly complicated. I'd run into problems like this: I'd try putting a red star in one of the empty squares and I'd find this opened up five new paths. I would trace four of the paths and find they led to loops or dead ends. I'd think that was great, because I now had more false paths. Then I'd trace the fifth path and find it led to the goal. This was no good; so I'd have to go back and try something besides a red star in that square. Eventually I got the maze to work, and it still has a lot of false paths. Some of these paths I had planned for, but most of them just took off on their own.

Solution to Maze 18:
Spacewreck!
Figure 4 shows the route to the goal. You start with one pencil on A and the other on B. This is shown in figure 4 by an A over a B. Next is an A over a G. This means that one pencil stayed on the A and the other pencil moved to the G. And so on.

Solution to Maze 19:
Meteor Storm
Figure 5 is a map that shows every path through this maze. The maze starts with one pencil on A and the other on B. This is shown on the map by an A over a B. From that starting state you can move right on the map to the state A-G, or you could follow an arrow down to the states A-C or F-B. Those two states are dead ends. Also, from the starting state you can follow an arrow up and over to the state E-B, then on another move you can go left on the map to the state E-F, and so forth. The shortest path to the goal is shown in red.

This map is a good indication of the complexity of the maze, a complexity that is not at all apparent in the original layout of the maze. If you actually solved this maze, you are probably *too* smart.

Solution to Maze 20:
Theseus and the Minotaur
In figure 6, I labeled the columns and rows of the maze so I can point out where things are.

To solve this maze, you have to maneuver the Minotaur into various traps. First you get him to go into the "cup" at square C4. Next you trap him on the west side of the wall between columns E and F. Then the Minotaur is trapped in the cup made up of squares L2 and M2. The next traps are on the east side of the wall between columns L and M, then in the cup at square G2, and finally on the *west* side of the wall between columns L and M.

The trickiest of these traps is the cup containing squares L2 and M2. Since that cup is right next to the exit, you might not consider trapping the Minotaur there. Theseus cannot, of course, escape when the

Figure 4   A A J J O O N N H H D D A A J J O O N N H H D D D A A J J O O N T T U U V V W W A A A A Z Z Y Y Y Goal

B G G K K F F B B G G K K F F B B G G K K F F B C C L L Q Q P P P N N H H D D A A J J O O N T

39

Minotaur is sitting next to the exit. But that trap will lead to subsequent traps.

The next paragraph shows a series of moves that will get Theseus out of the labyrinth. The moves by Theseus are shown by lower-case letters that stand for north, south, east, or west. Following each move by Theseus are zero, one, or two moves by the Minotaur. The Minotaur's moves are shown by upper-case letters. The solution starts with Theseus making a mad dash *towards* the Minotaur.

nN - nNW - eWW - eWW - eWW - sWW - sWS. The Minotaur is now at D4 and Theseus is directly below him at D5. wW-s-s-s-s-eES-eSE-eSS-n. Theseus is now at F8, the Minotaur is at E8, and the Minotaur is trapped behind the wall that separates him and Theseus. We're now in the most complex part of the labyrinth. From here there are many false paths that look like they'll get Theseus out of the labyrinth, but they don't quite make it. The true path continues as follows: nN-nN-nN-nN-e-e-nNE-nEE. Theseus is now at H2 and the Minotaur at H3.eE-eE-eE-n-eE-eE-eEN. Theseus is now at N1 and the Minotaur at N2. wW- wW-w-s-w-w-w-s-s-s-s-s-s-e-e-e-e-eE-eES-wWS. The Minotaur is now at M4 and Theseus is at M9. At this point Theseus waits out a turn, letting the Minotaur make two more moves to the south. SS-wSS-n. Theseus is now at L8 and the Minotaur at M8. nN-nN-n-w-w-w-w-nN-nNW-nWW-nNW- nWN. Theseus is now at H1 and the Minotaur is at H2. wW-w-s-s-s-s-s-s-s-e. Here comes another mad dash. Theseus must get past the wall between columns L and M before the Minotaur can catch him. eES-eES-eSE-eE-eES-eSS-n. Theseus is now at M8, the Minotaur is at L8 and trapped behind the wall, and Theseus now has an easy stroll to the exit. nN-nN-nN-n-n-e-n-e and out.

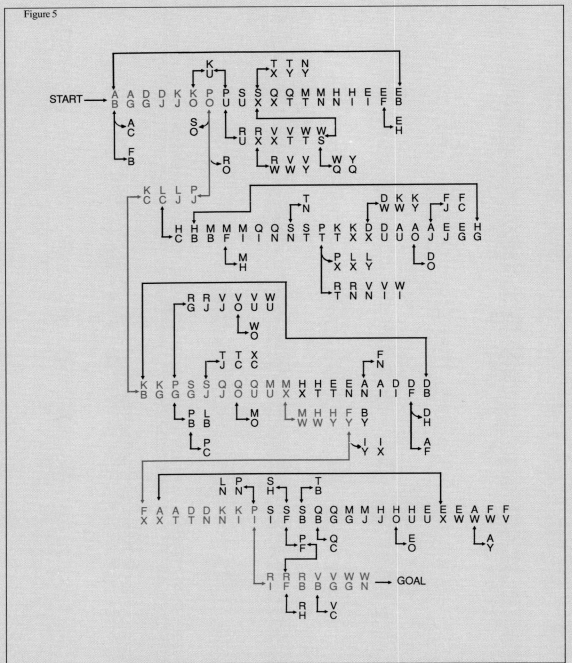

Figure 5

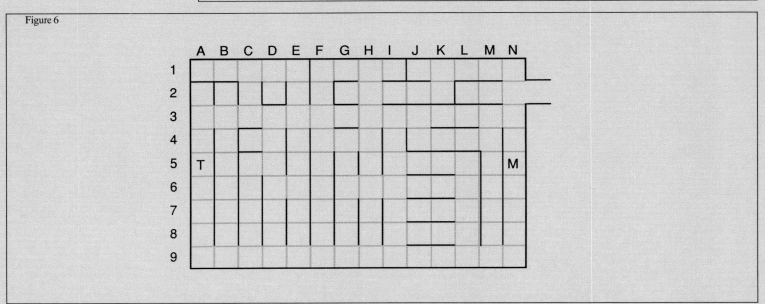

Figure 6